To Stephen

July 1989.

lots of love

From

Mrs. Fo...

Everyone
at St. Paul's Playgroup.

The Disneytime ANNUAL 1989

Contents

Published in Great Britain by London Editions Magazines. An Egmont Company.
Distributed by World International Publishing Limited, an Egmont Company, PO Box III, Great Ducie Street, Manchester M60 3BL.
ISBN 7235 6838 3
Printed in Italy

BAMBI TO THE RESCUE

1. Bambi and his friends Thumper, Rusty Squirrel and Freddy Frog had gone off exploring. At last they stopped to rest.

2. "Let's play hide-and-seek," Thumper suggested. So Bambi covered his eyes and counted while the others went off to hide.

3. "I can see you!" cried Bambi, after searching for ages, as Thumper peeped out of a rabbit hole to see what was going on.

4. Poor Bambi was even worse at hiding than seeking! He couldn't get down a hole, duck under water or climb a tree!

5. He felt so unhappy when his friends laughed at him. "What about leap-frog?" said Freddy. "Or hopscotch?" said Thumper.

6. And when it started to rain, everyone seemed to find shelter except Bambi. "I just wish I was back home," he sobbed.

7. But soon Thumper's rabbit hole became full of water, Freddy had to come up for air, and Rusty slid down the wet tree trunk.

8. The only dry land was under Bambi's body! "I'll say this for you," chuckled Rusty, "you make a fine umbrella!"

9. It wasn't long before the stream burst its banks and flooded the forest! "What shall we do?" cried Thumper. "We'll drown!"

10. "Quick, up on to my back, all of you," called Bambi. So Thumper hopped, Freddy leapt and Rusty climbed aboard.

11. Bambi was soon splashing through the forest to safety. "We're sorry we made fun of you earlier, Bambi," said Thumper.

12. "We're all good at different things," he added, "and you're best of all because you've saved us!" Bambi was happy at last!

WALT DISNEY'S

GOOFY, FOUNTAIN EXPERT

Hi, Goofy! What are you doing?

I'm building a park fountain, Horace! It'll be a beauty when I'm finished.

D 4580

The fountain figure is in this case!

Here, I'll help you!

Phew! This sure is heavy!

Yep! Thanks for the help, Horace! *PUFF! PANT!*

How's it going, Goofy?

Fine! I've nearly got it all connected up now!

Now all I have to do is turn the water on!

GASP!

SPLOSH!

You're quite an expert at this, aren't you!

THE PERFECT SNOWMAN

One day Pooh and Piglet went out on one of their walks. The previous night there had been a large snowfall and everywhere looked white and 'wintery'. As the two friends wandered along, they chatted to each other. Pooh always liked to discuss matters of great importance. "I wonder why snow is white," he said.

To which Piglet replied: "For the same reason that the sky is blue." This seemed to satisfy Pooh and they continued their walk.

Soon after they came across Roo, who was playing in the snow. Roo wanted to build a snowman but so far he really hadn't done very well. All that he had built was a pile of snow which looked more like a snow-castle than a snowman. "I don't suppose you could help me," said Roo to Pooh and Piglet. "I'm not doing very well by myself."

"Of course we can!" said Pooh. "What you need is a model to follow — something which is perfectly

formed and will stay still for hours." At that moment, Eeyore arrived, complaining about the weather . . .

"If there's one thing I don't like about the winter — it's the cold!" he grumbled.

"Here's our model," said Pooh. Eeyore looked puzzled.

"I've never been a model before," he said. "What do I have to do?"

"Well," replied Pooh, "in this case, you have to stand very still whilst we make a snowman, or rather a snow-Eeyore, using you as our model." The little donkey agreed, little realising what he had let himself in for. "Now remember," added Pooh, "you mustn't move an inch!" So while Eeyore stood there, Piglet, Roo and Pooh started to gather snow. Once they made a pile which was twice the size of Piglet they stopped and looked at Eeyore.

"Can I move yet?" he asked.

9

"Sorry, we won't be long now!" the others shouted. In a while they had gathered an enormous mound of snow, which they started to mould into an 'Eeyore-like' shape. At first they did rather well, because making the four legs turned out to be quite easy, however, the rest was not so simple. Try as they might, whenever they put a large lump of snow on to make the body, the legs always collapsed.

"Oh dear," said Pooh, "I think it would have been easier if we'd had someone else as a model." Eeyore mumbled to himself, he thought he was as good a model as anyone else.

"I'm never going to have a snowman!" said Roo and started to cry.

Pooh comforted his little friend. "Don't worry,

we'll think of something," he said, as he wondered what they could do next. Then Pooh remembered that Christopher Robin had once made a snowman which was almost perfect.

"Of course," he said, "come on, let's go and see Christopher Robin, he's bound to know how to make a proper snowman!"

When they arrived at Christopher Robin's house, Pooh told him everything that had happened. Christopher Robin couldn't help but smile when he imagined the four legs of snow. Of course, Christopher Robin knew exactly how to make a proper snowman. "First of all we shall need a carrot and some coal," he announced.

"Carrot and coal?" said Roo. "I thought you needed snow."

"A carrot for the nose and coal for the eyes. Rabbit will have a carrot and the Owl will have some coal," said Christopher Robin and he started organising his friends. Pooh set off to visit Rabbit and Piglet went to see Owl, whilst Christopher Robin looked after Roo.

In a while they all returned and Christopher Robin began to make the biggest snowman ever seen in Hundred Acre Wood. "First," said Christopher Robin, "you must make a very large snowball!" And he picked up two fistfuls of snow and pushed them together to make one large snowball. Then he gently put it down, and rolled it over in the snow. As the snowball turned, it collected more and more snow until it was almost the size of Pooh and he couldn't push it anymore. Then Christopher Robin made a slightly smaller snowball and, using all his strength, he placed it on top of the first one.

"There!" he said. "Now, Roo, will you add the eyes, mouth and nose and . . . it's finished!" The others stood back in wonder. It was the perfect snowman — only Christopher Robin could have been clever enough to build it. Roo was very happy.

The next day lots of other snowmen appeared all over Hundred Acre Wood, even Eeyore made one. But none of them was as good as the perfect snowman built by Christopher Robin.

USE THE SQUARES TO HELP YOU DRAW DONALD AGAIN

12

SCAMP'S TRICK

Scamp was a cheeky pup who was always playing tricks on his friends. One day he saw Pedro, the Mexican Chihuahua, looking at a bowl of food. Scamp felt very hungry, because he hadn't eaten all day. So he thought he would try a little trick.

"Morning, Pedro!" said Scamp as he went past. "That looks like a nice bowl of food."

"Hello, Scamp!" said Pedro. "Why don't you come over and have some?"

"That's very generous of you, I don't mind if I do," he said. So they both tucked into Pedro's food. "Thank you very much," said Scamp, licking his lips. Once he had gone, Pedro realised that crafty little Scamp had eaten nearly all his lunch.

Meanwhile, Scamp continued his walk. Next he came across his friend Jock, the terrier. He played exactly the same trick on him. Afterwards Jock too, noticed that Scamp had eaten nearly all his lunch.

Quite by chance, Pedro came by, just as Jock was wondering how to teach Scamp a lesson.

"Have you seen Scamp?" asked Pedro.

"Yes, he's just left, having eaten nearly all my lunch," replied Jock.

"He's just done that to me too! We ought to teach him a lesson!" said Pedro. The two dogs talked for a while, then ran as fast as they could to Scamp's house. There they saw exactly what they were hoping for — Scamp's lunch. Without wasting any time, Pedro and Jock tucked into it. A few moments later Scamp arrived.

"Hey, what's the big idea!" he shouted.

"Why, Scamp, we're taking our fair share of our lunches which you ate earlier today!" they said. When they'd stopped eating, Scamp was left with just a little bone in his bowl. The greedy little pup had been taught a lesson.

THE CAT BURGLARS

1. Many years ago, the rich Madame Adelaide lived in Paris with her cat Duchess and her kittens, Marie, Toulouse and Berlioz!

2. One day, when burglars broke into the mansion, even the brave and handsome Thomas O'Malley, Duchess's friend, was helpless.

3. You see, knowing the cats would protect their mistress's jewels, the cunning burglars sprayed them with pepper!

4. Now if there's one thing that cats hate, it's pepper. They leapt up and ran, sneezing and spluttering, from the mansion.

5. The burglars threw all Madame Adelaide's jewels into a sack and ran for their getaway car. But the engine wouldn't start!

6. Noticing Madame's carriage parked in the garage, they ordered Frou-Frou out of the stable to pull them to safety.

7. By now, the cats were miles away. "You naughty kittens," scolded Duchess, when she saw they had left a trail of wool behind them.

8. But that gave Thomas an idea. He leapt to the top of a tall tree and summoned the help of his alley cat friends.

9. The clever Frou-Frou followed the wool trail to where the cats where lying in wait. Then they dropped a net over the carriage.

10. Duchess and the kittens recovered the jewels while Thomas and his friends strung the net up from a high branch!

11. Madame Adelaide could hardly believe her ears when she heard what had happened. "This calls for a celebration," she said. So she threw the best party any of them could remember – with music from Scat Cat and The Wailers, of course!

ALICE'S STRANGE PARTY

Alice was a very polite girl, who quite by chance found herself in Wonderland. She had many amazing adventures there, and met many strange people, but none of them were as strange as the Mad Hatter and the March Hare.

Alice walked into a garden where there was a table set for tea. "I must say," she thought, "it would be very nice to have some tea, but I can't sit down until I'm asked to." She looked around and saw a very strange-looking hare with an even more peculiar man wearing a large hat. "Good day to you!" she said.

"That's as maybe," snapped the hare, "but we don't all have to agree with you. It may not be a good day."

"That's not very nice," replied Alice, "I was only being polite."

"Hoity-toity!" shouted the man. "And what would you be called?"

Alice was just about to tell him, when the hare interrupted and told her not to bother telling him as he couldn't give two hoots. The hare then introduced himself as the March Hare and the man as the Mad Hatter. "And if you want to be friends with us, please don't go on about it being a good day."

Alice looked at the tea on the table. "If I don't mention it's a good day, may I have some tea?" she asked.

"You may have anything, except the birthday

cake," shouted the Hatter. "That's mine!" It was a strange cake with only one candle on it.

"Is it your birthday cake?" Alice asked. "Are you one year old?" She was somewhat puzzled because the Hatter certainly didn't look one year old.

"Of course I'm not one year old, you silly girl!" screamed the Hatter. "What a funny friend you are!"

"You're the one who's silly," said Alice, "fancy having one candle on your cake, when you're older than a year."

"What do you mean?" screeched the Hatter. "This isn't a cake, it's a hat!" And he picked it up and put it on his head. "Now, because it's a hat, it doesn't matter how many candles I have. I can be as old as I like and still have just one candle!" he added.

"But you said it was a birthday cake," said Alice. "You're quite mad!"

"Of course I am," said the man. "That's why they call me the Mad Hatter!" And he skated round the room as if he was on ice — a very clever trick, considering that he was really on paving stones.

Then Alice sat down at the table, where she had tea. The others joined her, but they stayed as mad as ever. Nonetheless, Alice felt much better after her tea. She thanked them, and told them she must be on her way, but neither the March Hare or the Mad Hatter took much notice, they were trying to wake the dormouse, who was asleep in the teapot.

As Alice left, she thought what very strange people they were, but kind to give her tea. Later in Wonderland, Alice would meet much stranger people who were not nearly so kind. When she returned home she always remembered the Mad Hatter and the March Hare, every time she poured out a cup of tea.

DAME FOR A LAUGH

Is this a second hand shop?
Yes.
Excellent, I'll have one for my watch.

Girls' faults are many,
Boys have only two:
Everything they say,
And everything they do.

English teacher: Construct a sentence using the word archaic. *Tommy:* We can't have archaic and eat it.

Patient: Have you got anything for my liver?
Doctor: How about onions and gravy.

People who cough loudly never go to the doctor, they go to the cinema instead.

SIGN OUTSIDE A CHURCH:
TODAY'S SERMON
WHAT IS HELL?
COME AND LISTEN TO
OUR NEW ORGAN.

What do you need to know before you teach a dog tricks?
More than the dog.

STOP PRESS...

Lord Justice Turn-Up, yesterday imposed a 2 year suspended sentence on a pair of braces, after they held up a pair of trousers in a dark alley.

Customer: Waiter, there's a button in my tomato. *Waiter:* Oh, the salad dressing must have lost it.

WHAT DO YOU CALL A GUN WITH THREE BARRELS?
A TRIFLE.

What did the fortune teller say to the Geranium?
You are going to meet a tall, dark Hydrangea.

What did the thief say to the watch-seller?
Sorry to take so much of your valuable time.

THE BUSH MONSTER

1. A lot of rain had fallen recently in the jungle, which meant that the river was just right for Mowgli to relax in.

2. But the boy was suddenly startled by trumpeting elephants and monkeys calling and swinging wildly from tree to tree.

3. Mowgli had been brought up by the animals and knew they were signs of danger. "I must hurry," he quickly decided.

4. Out of the trees came Colonel Hathi of the elephant patrol and Louie, King of the Monkeys. "What's up?" ask Mowgli.

5. "A-a **m-monster** – and it isn't Shere Khan!" said Louie. "A **walking bush**!" added the Colonel. "And it's heading this way!"

6. "Oh, is it now?" said Bagheera, the wise panther. "And might I ask if anyone has seen Baloo today?" No one had.

7. "Maybe we can soon solve this mystery," smiled Bagheera. "Help me tie this long, strong reed between two trees, Mowgli."

8. The trap was set and they all hid as the strange creature approached. It did look very much like a **bush monster**!

9. Nearer and nearer it came, then tripped over the reed, just as Bagheera had planned, and splashed into the river!

10. And who should climb out but a very wet Baloo! "**You**!" gasped Louie. "Fancy scaring us like that!" scolded the Colonel.

11. "He didn't mean to," explained Bagheera. "You fell into a muddy bog, then leaves and twigs stuck to you – right, Baloo?" Of course, Baloo couldn't remember! But he would remember the party to celebrate the end of the bush monster for a long time!

HOLIDAY ADVENTURE

Donald and his nephews have gone on a sailing holiday. They've set their sights on reaching Paradise Island. However, before they get there a few surprises are in stall for them. See if you and your friends can help them reach the island. Take a counter each and a dice, then move according to your throws with the dice. You must obey all the instructions on the squares. The first one to land on the island is the winner. So splice that mainbrace! Raise that anchor and set sail with Donald and the boys!

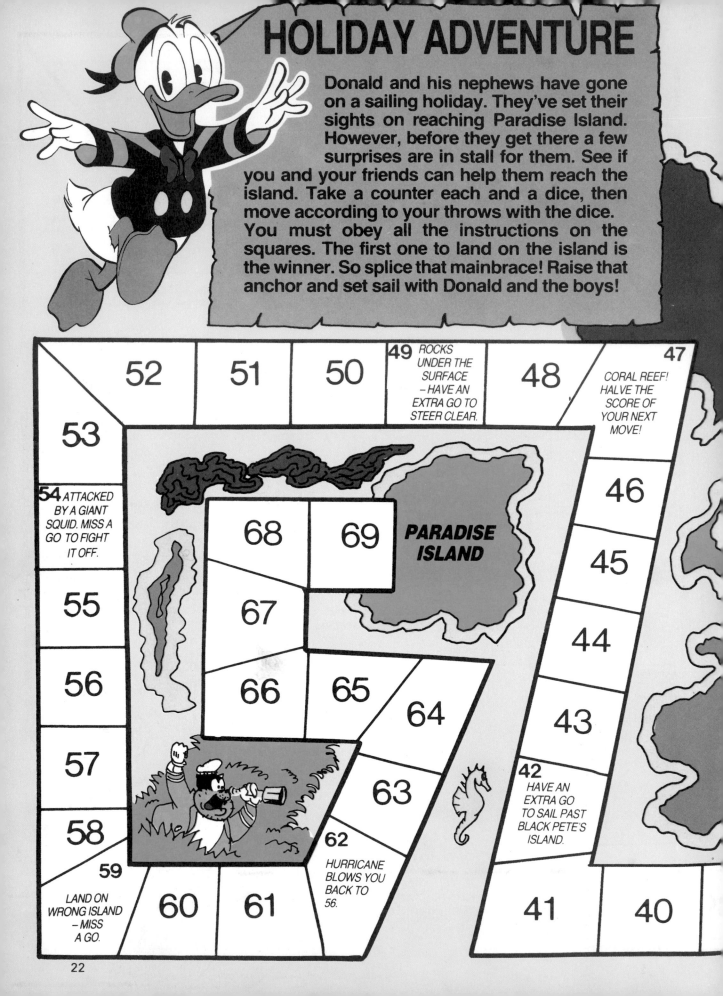

52 51 50

49 ROCKS UNDER THE SURFACE – HAVE AN EXTRA GO TO STEER CLEAR.

48

47 CORAL REEF! HALVE THE SCORE OF YOUR NEXT MOVE!

53

54 ATTACKED BY A GIANT SQUID. MISS A GO TO FIGHT IT OFF.

46

45

68 69

PARADISE ISLAND

67

55

44

56

66 65

64

43

57

63

42 HAVE AN EXTRA GO TO SAIL PAST BLACK PETE'S ISLAND.

58

62 HURRICANE BLOWS YOU BACK TO 56.

59 LAND ON WRONG ISLAND – MISS A GO.

60 61

41 40

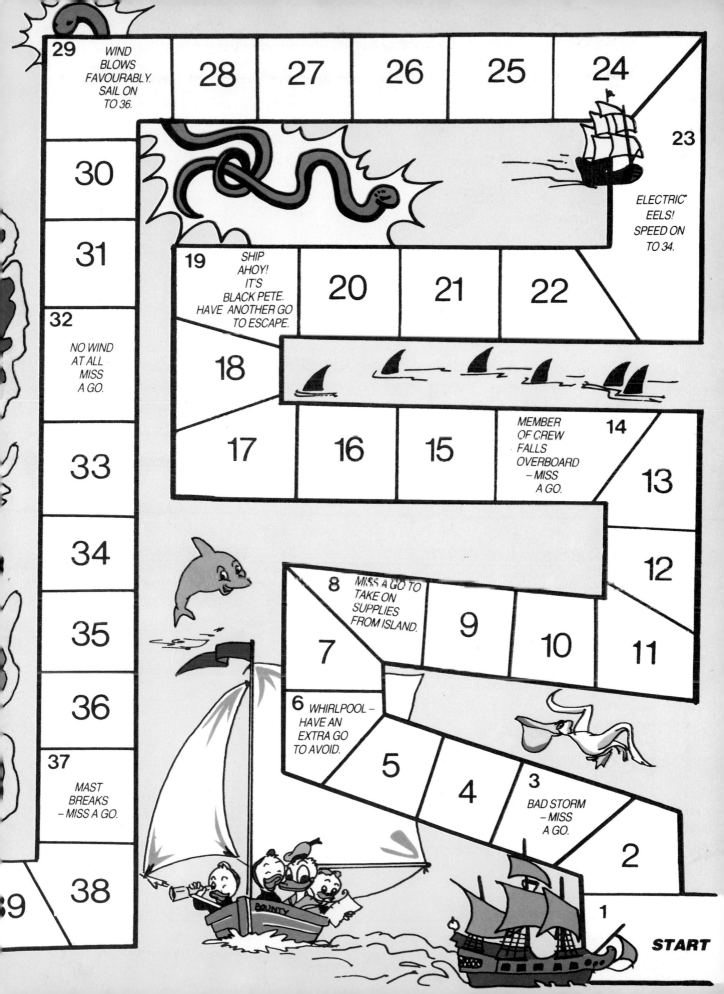

DUMBO'S COLD

Dumbo and his friend Timothy Mouse worked in a circus. Dumbo the flying elephant was famous throughout the land for his flying feats and people came from miles around just to see him. On this particular day, everyone else in the circus was working hard to get things ready for the evening performance. Meanwhile Dumbo and Timothy were having a quiet snooze underneath a tree. They were woken by the sound of hammers knocking the mighty tent pegs of the big top into the ground.

Timothy Mouse yawned, clambered up Dumbo's body and perched himself inside Dumbo's hat. "Wake up, wake up!" he shouted. "What a show it's going to be tonight — the biggest of the year."

Dumbo opened his eyes slightly, then went back to sleep. Timothy nudged him again and this time Dumbo sneezed. It made a funny sound like someone blowing a trumpet very loudly. But even this didn't wake the little elephant. So Timothy tried again, but Dumbo just sneezed a second time — even more loudly! The force of this sneeze blew Timothy to the ground.

"Oh my, Dumbo must have a very bad cold," said Timothy. "When he gets colds, his ears go all floppy and he can't fly. Tonight it's the biggest show of the year, if Dumbo doesn't perform, he could lose his job, and I'd lose mine. It would be a disaster!" Meanwhile, Dumbo slept on. All around, the noise of the circus continued, lions roared, clowns practised and seals barked.

Timothy was getting very worried. He wrapped a scarf around Dumbo's neck and covered him with a blanket, whilst he thought what to do next. He decided to let him sleep on and went to ask some of his friends if they knew of a cold cure.

First of all, he asked the seals; they suggested that Dumbo should eat lots of raw fish, but Timothy told them that his friend didn't like raw fish at all. The lions suggested that he stop eating buns, but buns were Dumbo's favourite food and Timothy didn't have the heart to deny his little friend his favourite food.

So he walked back to where he had left Dumbo and was amazed to find him awake and not wearing his scarf. Dumbo rubbed his eyes with his feet and said: "Hello, Timothy, I wondered where you'd got

to. I was going to tell you about this strange dream I had. I was at the South Pole visiting some penguins. It was so cold down there, I kept sneezing all the time … anyway, after a while my ears started to freeze up, but a kind penguin called Pablo looked after me and warmed me up with his stove, so I was able to fly back home."

Timothy was dumbstruck. "You mean you didn't really have a cold."

"No," said Dumbo, "I told you it was only a dream."

That evening, the show went ahead and all the audience loved Dumbo the flying elephant. Little did they realise what had happened earlier in the day, but Timothy Mouse knew and he smiled as he watched Dumbo soaring high above the crowd.

26

28

How to be a ☆ *SORCERER'S* ☆ APRENTICE ✶

Donald has put on his magician's hat to become 'The Great Donaldo'. He has learnt quite a few tricks – see if you can learn how to do them, then try them out on your friends.

The Moving Match

Stand a 10p or 50p coin on its edge, balance a spent book match on top and place a glass over both of them. Tell the audience that the match is very unhappy in the glass and it's trying to get out. You can show how it moves by taking a comb, running it through your hair a few times and holding it right up to the glass. You should see the match moving.

The Vanishing Paper Clip

Have you noticed that paper clips have a nasty habit of disappearing? Well, in this trick you can show people how it happens, right under their noses – one minute it's there, the next it's gone! Attach a rubber band to the paper clip, with the other end safety-pinned about 10 centimetres up your jacket sleeve. Hold the paper clip with the back of your hand to the audience so the rubber band cannot be seen. When you release the clip, it will snap back up your sleeve and disappear.

THE HAPPY HANDKERCHIEF

This one always gets a few laughs.... Tell the audience that every now and then your handkerchief needs a bit of fresh air, so take it and bounce it off the floor.

What they don't know is that you have sewn a bouncy ball into the middle of your handkerchief. So you can bounce it anywhere you like.

A Lot of Bottle

Make a hoop from some stiff paper and stand it on the mouth of an empty wine bottle. Place a small coin, a 1p bit will do, on top of the hoop, above the neck of the bottle and challenge anyone from the audience to get the coin inside the bottle.

After they have tried and probably failed, you can show them how to do it. Give the inside of the hoop a swift blow from your wand. The hoop should spin away and the coin will fall into the bottle.

Here's a little teaser which always foxes people:
Which part of your body can your left hand touch but your right cannot?
It's your elbow!

31

A DAY ON THE RIVER

1. Cinderella got her name because the ugly sisters were jealous of her beauty and made her sleep by the hearth among the cinders.

2. One day, they left Cinders working as usual, while they went off punting in their fine gowns with their noble escorts.

3. But because she was so kind, Cinderella had a fairy godmother. "You shall go to the river, too," the good fairy told her.

4. "**Go to your old toybox and you'll find a boat. A quick spell from me and you'll soon be afloat!**" the fairy chanted.

5. Sure enough, when Cinderella opened her childhood toybox, there was a little rowing boat, complete with a team of oarsmen!

6. "Take it to the river," said the fairy. "But you must be back on dry land on the stroke of four." So Cinderella set off.

7. And, with a puff of smoke, the boat grew larger and dropped into the water and Cinderella was wearing a beautiful gown!

8. "Pray, allow me, my lady," said the leading oarsman, taking Cinderella's hand and helping her down into the boat.

9. She was soon being rowed along in style. As she flashed past the punts, the spray from her boat drenched her ugly sisters!

10. Cinderella stepped on to the bank on the stroke of four. Then **puff!** the boat became a toy again and she was back in rags!

11. She picked up the tiny toy and was back home in plenty of time to greet her wet and dishevelled ugly sisters.

12. "Aargh! That boat!" they gasped, recognizing it. "You wouldn't believe the fun it's given me today," laughed Cinderella.

CHAT SHOW DONALD

"Why does it always happen to me?" shouted Scrooge McDuck. He slammed the telephone down so hard that it made his secretary, Miss Typefast, drop the tray of biscuits she was carrying.

"What's wrong?" she asked, as she bent down to clear up the mess.

"What's wrong? What's wrong? I'll tell you what's wrong! My best star, the country's favourite chat show host, Perry Peterson, has just left my TV company to star in Glomgold's TV Spectacular. That's what's wrong!"

"There's no need to shout, Mr McDuck!" said Miss Typefast. " I still don't see why you're so angry — there are plenty of chat show hosts around."

"Maybe there are, but I need one for the show that starts in five hours time to interview Duckburg's greatest film star — Sylvia Shrimp," bawled Scrooge.

"In that case, may I make a suggestion?" said Miss Typefast. "Your nephew Donald was here earlier looking for a job."

"Donald! Why that's ridiculous — he couldn't tell a microphone from a microscope!" shouted Scrooge.

"At this late stage you can't be too fussy and besides, you won't have to pay him very much!" replied Miss Typefast.

At the mention of a bargain, Scrooge's eyes lit up. Within minutes he was on the phone to his nephew arranging to meet him at the studio: "Okay then, Donald, I'll see you at six, the show starts at seven. Don't be late."

* * *

Donald met Scrooge promptly at six in the TV studios. He was a little surprised that his uncle had offered him such an important job, as he usually gave Donald all the work no one else wanted. However, Donald had decided that he was going to do his very best.

Uncle Scrooge took Donald to his interview chair in the studio. It was surrounded by cameras. "Now this is where you sit," said Scrooge. "When that light comes on over a camera, then you should look into that camera — you won't have to learn any words because they're all written on these boards — they're called idiot boards. And remember, always be polite to your guest. Have you got all that? Good." Throughout his speech, Scrooge wandered up and down the studio, dodging cameras and scenery, whilst Donald nodded whenever he thought it was appropriate. Once he had finished, Scrooge rejoined Donald in the centre of the studio and reminded Donald again:

35

"Remember, be polite to your guest, she's a very famous film star!"

"Don't worry, you can depend on me," said Donald.

"I hope so," said Scrooge. "Now, go to your dressing room and wait for me to call you."

* * *

Donald had been waiting in his dressing room for a while, when there was a knock on the door. A voice shouted: "Five minutes, Mr Donald!"

"If I had nails, I'd bite 'em!" said Donald to himself. "Boy, am I nervous." After what seemed ages, Donald was called into the studio. When he got there he couldn't see very much because of the bright lights, however, he could hear the audience and see the five cameras staring back at him. As he sat down in his chair, Donald saw Scrooge with one of his boards, it said: "Keep calm, Donald!"

Then all the lights went out and a voice boomed: "AS YOUR HOST TONIGHT, WITH SPECIAL GUEST, SYLVIA SHRIMP . . . HERE'S DONALD!"

The music started, the audience cheered loudly and Donald thought: "I'm going to enjoy this." When all the noise had died down, Donald looked into the first camera and read the words from the board: "And now let me introduce Duckburg's greatest film star, who has just flown in from Duckapaulco . . . Miss . . ."

Donald never finished his sentence because Sylvia Shrimp arrived on stage. Donald thought he'd better be polite and show her to her seat. The cheering grew louder as Donald greeted her. "Boy, this is fun," he said to himself.

Once Sylvia was seated, Donald tried his first question. "When did you start in films, Miss . . .?"

Suddenly Donald had to change cameras and instead of saying "Miss Shrimp," he said "Miss Shrump."

Miss Shrimp was not impressed, no one ever got her name wrong. "What did you call me?" she bawled. Poor Donald became even more confused and looked back at the boards for another question. Unfortunately it began with the words: "An Old Woman in Venice was your first film . . ." so Donald started . . .

"An old woman . . ." But before he could continue, the film star became outraged and shouted at him.

"Never in all my years have I been so insulted. How dare you call me an old woman?" Now Donald, who had kept his temper up to this point, began to shout back.

"I never liked any of your stupid films anyway!" he

fumed. After that, all Donald could remember was being hit over the head with a handbag and Scrooge shouting that he was fired.

* * *

A week later Uncle Scrooge sat in his office. He was still furious with Donald for ruining his TV show. Suddenly, Miss Typefast came in clutching a copy of the Duckburg Times.

"Have you seen this?" she said excitedly, "Donald's show topped the ratings last week. Everyone said it was the funniest programme they'd seen for ages." Without wasting a second, Scrooge rang Donald.

"Ah, Donald . . . I was wondering if you'd fancy doing another wee show for me," he said.

Donald's reply made Uncle Scrooge slam down the phone. "Sorry, Uncle Scrooge, but I'm already booked to host Glomgold's Spectacular!"

Snow White and the Seven PUZZLES

While the Dwarfs were out digging, Snow White thought it would be fun to invent a puzzle for each of her seven little friends. See how many you can answer.

1 Can you fill in the missing number?

5	7

3	6	5	4

3 See if you can find your way through the maze.

2 Without using a pencil see if you can say which one of these three balloons will actually reach the landing target.

4 How many fish have been caught in this net?

5 Fill in the missing letters to make words down and the name of a forest animal across.

E	M	O	E	P	O
B	P	D	G	N	E

6 Can you answer these three questions?
What do you call a baby deer?
Can you give the proper name for a hole where a rabbit lives?
Conkers have another name, what is it?

7 Unscramble

N O A M D I D

to give you the name of a precious stone.

ANSWERS

1. The missing number is 6. 2. The right balloon is number 2. 4. 16 5. Badger 6. A fawn, a warren and a horse chestnut. 7. Diamond

WINNIE THE POOH'S FAVOURITE FOOD

As everyone knows Winnie the Pooh's favourite food is honey. But believe it or not, Pooh occasionally eats other things apart from honey. Christopher Robin sometimes cooks for him and when he does, these are Pooh's favourites.... try them at home!

HONEY AND GINGER SHORTBREAD

Ingredients
6oz (175g) plain flour
3oz (85g) butter
1oz (25g) caster sugar
3 rounded tablespoons set honey
4oz (100g) crystallized ginger

1. Preheat the oven at 160°C/325°F/ Gas 3 – you'd better ask your mum or dad to do this for you – and grease a baking tray.
2. Sift the flour into a bowl and rub in the butter. Add the sugar, honey and chopped ginger and mix.
3. Knead the mixture lightly, folding it from the outside to the centre, until the dough is firm and smooth.
4. Divide the dough into three equal portions and roll out into circles about 7" (18cm) across.
5. Pinch the edges between thumb and finger and mark each circle into 8 with a carving knife, and put on the baking tray.
6. Bake for about 20 minutes until crisp and golden, then leave to cool on the tray and sprinkle with sugar.

QUICK CUP CAKE

To make this cake is quick and easy you don't even have to weigh the ingredients.
You will need:

1 cup milk
1 cup dried mixed fruit
1 cup brown sugar
2 cups self-raising flour
1 teaspoon mixed spice

1. Preheat the oven to 180°C/350°F/Gas 4.
2. Grease a 1lb (450g) loaf tin.
3. Using a good-size tea cup, measure all the ingredients into a large mixing bowl.
4. Mix well using a wooden spoon.
5. Put the mixture into the loaf tin and bake for 1 hour.
6. Serve in slices and add butter if you like.

SPOTS BEFORE THE EYES

1. While the Dalmatians' master, Roger, was away on business, their mistress, Anita, was planning a surprise for him.

2. "A decorator is painting the outside of the house and an artist is going to paint a portrait of you all," she told them.

3. The puppies were looking their best when the artist arrived and began painting. "Keep quite still now," he told them.

4. They were ready for a break by coffee time. "Just remember your positions, please," the artist called to them.

5. The puppies didn't even remember that the decorator's paint would be outside, and crashed into a table with a paint tin on it!

6. When he resumed, the artist couldn't understand why some of the models were still spotted and some were pure white!

7. At lunchtime, the puppies avoided the table, but instead bumped into a ladder and some more paint plopped on to them!

8. "I don't believe it!" gasped the artist after lunch. "Now some of you are spotted, some are white and some are black!"

9. "Seeing spots before my eyes is driving me crazy!" he raged. "I can't take any more!" Then he raced out of the door!

10. Anita was cross at first, but she soon had to laugh. "I said you were going to be painted," she said, "but not like that!"

11. After a good wash, the puppies went with Anita to buy Roger a present, which he opened when he returned. "A camera!" he gasped.

12. Can you guess what was the very first photograph Roger took? "This knocks spots off a painting any day!" he laughed.

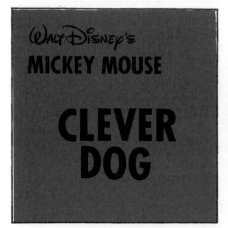

GEPPETTO'S STORY

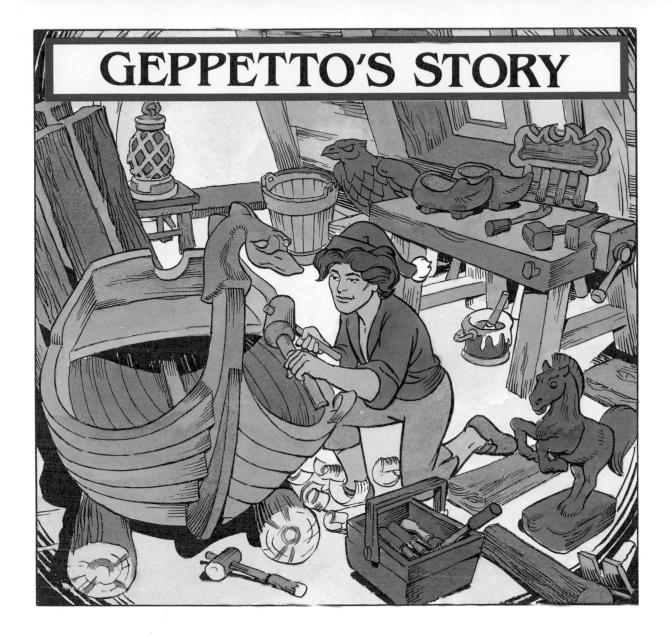

Every evening before bedtime, Geppetto used to tell Pinocchio a story. On this blustery winter's evening, he told him the story of Peter the carpenter.

Peter lived a long time ago, in a country ruled by a stern but wise king. For many years Peter had worked hard as a carpenter, and all agreed that his work was the finest in the land, but he was very poor and lived in a little cottage all by himself. He used to dream of the day when he would live in a large warm house with a wife who loved him. Then one day a strange thing happened which was to change Peter's life for ever.

He was walking along a country road late one evening, after he'd spent a day collecting wood in the forest. Suddenly he was attacked by two thieves, who knocked him to the ground. The robbers set about removing his purse, but stopped when they heard a coach pull up. A voice shouted out: "In the name of the King unhand that man!" The thieves turned and fled. As Peter got up and walked towards the coach, he was surprised to see a young woman get out.

"Was it you who called out just then?" he asked.

"Yes, it was a trick my father taught me," said the woman.

"Then tell me who your father is and who you are, so that I might thank you both!" Peter said.

"My father is the King, so you can guess who I am . . ."

"You must be Princess Auburnia!" Peter said. He fumbled in his pocket and produced a wooden brooch in the shape of a bird. "Here, take this as thanks, I don't suppose I will be visiting the palace very often." Auburnia blushed slightly, thanked Peter and returned to her carriage. As she waved goodbye, Peter wondered if he would see anyone so beautiful ever again.

* * *

Many months later Peter received a strange letter. It came from the Royal Palace and asked Peter to present himself at the court in a week's time with a gift for the Princess's birthday. He had no money to buy anything, so he decided to carve a statue out of wood. Before he began, he had no idea what he would make, but gradually his hands did the work for him and without realising it, he carved a perfect likeness of the Princess he had met many months ago. He even gave the statue a brooch exactly like the one he had given to the Princess.

A week later he went to the palace. When he got there he found two other well-dressed young men. These men were bearing gifts too, but their's looked a great deal more costly than Peter's. Peter felt ashamed of his old shabby clothes and humble gift. The King greeted all three of them and asked them in turn to present their gifts.

One of the well-dressed men went first. He gave the King a gold cup decorated with a silver pattern.

The King took it and disappeared behind a screen that stood at the side of the court. After a moment, he reappeared and asked the young man: "Tell me, how did you come across this cup?"

"I paid the goldsmith to make me the most valuable gift he had ever made," he replied.

"Well, it is not a gift that we would like. Goodbye!" said the King. The next man presented his gift, which was a gown made of purple silk and enormous pearls. Exactly the same thing happened, the King returned from behind the screen and asked where he had come across the gown, to which the second man replied . . .

"I told my servants to travel to distant lands until they found the most exotic garment money could buy." He too, was asked to leave the court. This left Peter with his wooden statue. The King looked at the statue and smiled. He went behind the screen

and this time a different, slightly familiar voice asked the question. To which Peter gave his honest answer . . .

"I had no money to buy a gift, so I carved it with my own hands."

To Peter's surprise and joy, Auburnia appeared from behind the screen with the King. She explained to Peter how she had lost her heart to him that night when they first met. But, when she told her father about him, he refused to let her see him, as he thought a poor man was no match for a princess. So it was, that she devised a way to prove to her father that Peter was indeed worthy of her hand . . .

The King could see that Peter's gift was made with love and that he would be a perfect husband for his beloved only daughter.

Not long afterwards, a Royal marriage took place . . . and all Peter's dreams had come true.

A DAY OF SURPRISES

1. Snow White agreed to keep house for the dwarfs only if they did all the outside work. But they didn't like doing it at all!

2. For ages she had been asking them to clear the garden before winter. Then one morning Doc said, "Today's the day!"

3. Snow White watched them march away from the house carrying all kinds of garden tools and pushing a wheelbarrow.

4. Later, she looked out of the window and saw them still hard at work in the distance. "I'll take them some lunch," she decided.

5. "Funny," thought Snow White, walking towards them. "It's the woodland creatures working – and the dwarfs are quite still!"

6. "No wonder," she cried, "they're **cardboard** dwarfs! I've been tricked! Right! **Eight** can play at that game!"

7. Meanwhile, the dwarfs were busy in their mine. "I wonder how **we're** getting on?" laughed Doc. "Nearly finished, I hope!"

8. They returned home from work at the usual time, feeling as hungry as ever! "Yoo-hoo! We're home!" they chuckled.

9. "Had a busy day?" asked Snow White "We sure have," said Happy. "But everything's finished outside for the winter."

10. "Mmm, smells as if you've been busy, too," sneezed Sneezy. "Oh, I have . . . I have!" said Snow White. "Dinner's all ready!"

11. "URGH!" they cried, taking their first bites. "**Cardboard** meat . . . potatoes . . . peas!" "For **cardboard dwarfs**!" said Snow White.

12. But she gave them their real dinners when they promised never to trick her again. For once, they **all** felt **dopey**!

THE DUCKBURG TIMES

ISSUE 1

SUPER GOOF HERO SAVES DOOMED ELEPHANT

Yesterday, Super Goof was once again the toast of Duckburg, after he had rescued an elephant which was falling to certain death. The incident occurred soon after lunchtime, when passers-by noticed an elephant perched precariously on a 10th floor window ledge.

The police were immediately called, but the elephant, named Clara, refused to come down. After several hours, during which Clara was passed food, consisting mainly of several hundred sticky buns, Chief O'Hara managed to find out why she had taken such a dramatic course of action.

It transpired that she was depressed after being sacked from her job at the local circus. She said she no longer had any means to support herself, and wished to end it all.

Just as she finished these words, a sudden gust of wind blew her off and she seemed to be plummeting to her death. When from nowhere, the caped wonder Super Goof plucked Clara from the sky, and set her down safely in a nearby field.

The crowds cheered as Super Goof sped through the skies, back to his secret hide-out. All ended happily, when another benevolent circus owner offered Clara a job, as chief performing elephant.

○ *Super Goof to the rescue*

BEAGLE BOYS IN BIZARRE BUSINESS

The citizens of Duckburg can sleep in their beds tonight, safe in the knowledge that the city's most infamous felons, the Beagle Boys, are asleep in a prison cell.

All three of them were apprehended last night by police as they tried to break into the Duckburg City Bank. Such an incident would not have been unusual, were it not for the bizarre costumes which the brothers were wearing.

Each of them was disguised as a bank safe, in a costume made out of old eggbox cartons and cardboard boxes. However, their plans fell through when they discovered that their costumes were wider than the bank's doors. As they struggled to get through, they set off the alarms, and they were all swiftly arrested.

GYRO'S SCIENTIFIC SENSATION

Gyro Gearloose has revealed his latest invention, a pencil which never goes blunt. After months of research, Gyro came

○ *Gyro and his Little Helper.*

across something which lead him to his discovery, a manmade material which replenishes itself, as soon as it wears away. Not everyone, however, was pleased with the announcement. A spokesman for the pencil industry had this to say:

"To put it bluntly, we don't see the point of it". But Gyro still has a few problems with the idea. His prototype never-ending pencil is 1 foot round and 6 feet long, so it might be a while before you see one in the shops!

Pluto Wins Canine Competition

Mickey Mouse's dog Pluto scooped first prize in this year's Duckburg Dog Show.

Over 300 entrants competed in a series of rounds designed to test the overall ability and appearance of each dog.

Pluto came first in all the rounds except for obedience, where Mickey found Pluto more than a handful, after he had spied a small cat in the audience.

Following a long chase through the back row of seats in the arena, Pluto eventually cornered the petrified mog.

However, to the relief of everyone present, all Pluto wished to do, was to meet the cat, whose father had once removed a thorn from his paw, when he was just a pup.

The judges were so impressed, they awarded him first prize.

○ *Pluto – top of the dogs!*

DONALD AND GLADSTONE IN DISPUTE

Duckburg's normally quiet streets were, yesterday, disrupted by an unseemly row involving two old rivals, Donald Duck and Gladstone Gander. The argument over who should take Miss Daisy to the opera, erupted into violence, when Gladstone let the tyres down on Donald's new car.

Donald reacted by filling Gladstone's bath with treacle. Both were trying to prevent the other from turning up at Daisy's house on the night of the concert.

In an act of wild desperation, Donald and Gladstone rammed each other with their cars. In the argument which followed, both of them raised their voices to such a level that neighbours had to call the police.

Chief O'Hara then decided to settle the argument once and for all, by taking them round to Daisy's house, to let her make up her own mind.

When Daisy realised what had happened, she thought the two of them had behaved so stupidly, that she decided to take Chief O'Hara with her.

Last night, Donald and Gladstone were 'unavailable for comment', but Daisy and Chief O'Hara are reported to have thoroughly enjoyed themselves.

STOP PRESS...STOP PRESS...STOP

Big Bad Wolf was taken into hospital last night, after he had tried to capture the Little Pigs by using a giant wind machine. As he switched it on, the machine swung round and blew him into his own house.

Duckburg erupted into spontaneous parties this morning, as news came through, that Scrooge McDuck had given away some money to a person in need. This is the first time such a thing has happened in 20 years.

MICKEY'S MARVELS

Here are some hair-raising facts unearthed by Mickey with a touch of magic about them.

Witches used to think that a black spider sandwich was great protection against colds and common ailments.

Eating garlic is supposed to ward off witches... think about it, have you ever seen a vampire in Italy?

In olden times people used to break up egg shells, because they thought that witches used them to travel around.

Did you know that a bat can see in the dark by making tiny squeaks, which echo back to it. The pitch of the sound tells the bat how far away and how big an object is.
You may not see them but they can see you.

Britain is supposedly one of the most haunted countries in the world.

In 1740 a cow was found guilty of witchcraft.

All witches fear salt, because they think it is symbol of good.

All this information is based on folklore and should be taken with a pinch of salt — definitely not seriously!

BRAVE SCAMP

One day Scamp was playing outside with his sisters. He always liked to pretend that he was a clever pup and would show off by doing tricks. Whilst Scamp was practising one of his tricks — balancing a ball on the end of his nose — a large Alsatian came up and started laughing. The noise put Scamp off and he dropped the ball.

"What are you laughing at?" asked Scamp.

"You and your silly games," said the Alsatian. "I can do tricks twice as good as that."

"Go on then, let's see you!" said Scamp.

So the Alsatian flicked up the ball with his paw and balanced it on his nose, then he started to bounce it up and down before finally knocking it into an empty dustbin.

"Well done!" said Scamp's sisters.

"That's nothing, I'm sure I can do even better!" said Scamp. So, while the others looked on, Scamp ran off, got the ball and perched himself on top of it. For a while he managed to stay on as the ball rolled over. But it started to move more quickly and Scamp found himself rolling towards a great big puddle. SPLOSH! went Scamp as he landed in the mud. Scamp's sisters started laughing and the big Alsatian couldn't help but smile.

"Well, Scamp. I can see that you've been practising that trick for a long time!" he said. "Why don't you see if you can do this one . . . ?" Next to where they were playing, there were some builders' pipes, which were quite narrow, but wide enough for a dog to run down. "Come on," shouted the Alsatian, "follow me!"

Scamp ran over as quickly as he could, determined not to be shown up in front of his sisters. He followed the larger dog, in and out of the pipes, but very soon he got dizzy, turning from side to side and hopping in and out. In no time at all, the Alsatian had finished the race and poor Scamp was left breathless and dazed.

"Well done, well done!" said Scamp's sisters to the Alsatian. "You're very brave and clever, where did you learn to do that?"

"Oh, that was nothing really, we used to do things like that all the time in the Police Service!"

"You mean you were in the Police? Gosh, then you must be very brave and strong. I wish our Scamp was like you!" said one of Scamp's sisters. Poor Scamp could only look on in dismay.

While all this was going on, no one had noticed a large alley cat come up behind them. One of Scamp's sisters saw it first and started yelping. "Quick," said the others to the Alsatian, "frighten it away." The alley cat screeched and arched its back at the Alsatian. The 'brave' Police dog, instead of helping Scamp's sisters, just ran away!

"I'm sorry," he cried, "but I'm frightened of cats!" At that moment, Scamp saw what was going on and knew he must help his sisters. So he stood up inside the pipe and started to growl. Because he was inside the pipe the cat couldn't see him, and the growling noise grew louder and fiercer as it echoed around the pipe. The alley cat thought it was a ferocious dog that was just about to pounce, so it ran away as fast as it could.

"That Alsatian wasn't brave," said Scamp's sisters, "you're truly brave, Scamp!"

A CLOSE SHAVE

1. Pinocchio watched as Geppetto, the wood carver, worked away. "I can never make things and be a real assistant," he sighed.

2. "Oh, maybe one day . . . one day," smiled the old man. "Come on now!" It had been a long, hard day and he was very tired.

3. Geppetto was just nodding off when he remembered he hadn't swept up the shavings or closed the windows of the workshop.

4. "Please go and sweep up, then close up for me, Pinocchio," he asked. But by this time, Pinocchio was feeling tired, too.

5. "Go along," insisted Jiminy Cricket, pushing Pinocchio towards the door. "Real assistants always do as they are asked."

6. But before he could sweep up all the wood shavings or close the windows, Pinocchio had fallen asleep himself!

7. The little boy didn't stir as a stream of busy visitors flew in and out of the open windows all night.

8. "Good, you swept up perfectly," said Geppetto, next morning. "I did?" said Pinocchio, surprised. "Y-yes, I did!"

9. But as he spoke, Pinocchio's nose began to grow longer. "Funny!" thought Geppetto. "I wonder what he did with the shavings?"

10. Then on their way to buy more wood, something strange happened. "It's **raining wood shavings**!" cried Geppetto.

11. "Now I understand," smiled Geppetto. "You helped make nests for the birds with the wood shavings! How very clever!"

12. Back at the workshop, Geppetto gave Pinocchio his very own apron. "You're a **real** assistant, after all," he smiled.

DAME FOR A LAUGH

Ha Ha!

Here are some of Daisy's favourite jokes....

Waiter, there's a button in my lunch.
Well you did ask for a jacket potato.

Ha Ha!

You're late again, Jenkins! Why don't you buy an alarm clock?
I did, sir, but it keeps going off while I'm asleep.

Graham, did your father help you with this homework?
No, sir, he did it all.

Tee Hee!

Mummy, I don't think I want to go to France.
Be quiet, dear, and start swimming!

What happened to the man who dreamt he was eating a large marshmallow?
He woke up and found that his pillow had gone.

Giggle

Chortle!

What did the boy magnet say to the girl magnet?
I find you very attractive!

How many feet are there in a yard?
That depends on how many people are standing in it!

Why is it impossible to buy dentures in a shop?
Because you shouldn't pick your teeth in public.

Tee Hee!

55

DUMBO AND THE SEAL

One of Dumbo's best friends at the circus was Sammy the Seal. This is the story of what happened when Sammy went missing and how Dumbo found him.

Sammy the seal was very popular, he was always cheerful and knew how to do lots of tricks. At feeding time Sammy used to catch the fish in his mouth, but he never took more than his fair share.

One morning the other seals noticed that Sammy had gone missing, they all started barking furiously. Lots of the circus folk gathered round, they soon realised what was wrong. Everyone began searching the circus for any sign of Sammy — but they found nothing. Dumbo flew over the big top, but even he couldn't see anything.

"It's no good!" said the circus manager.

"Sammy's gone for good. Come on, everyone, let's get ready for tonight's show." They all trudged back to their tents. Dumbo and Timothy Mouse sat down by a tree near the seal pond.

"What can we do?" said Dumbo. "We can't just forget about Sammy. He could be in serious trouble!"

"You're right," agreed Timothy. "We must do something. Maybe the other seals know where he's gone?" So they went over to the seal pool and asked Sydney — the oldest seal — if he had any ideas about where Sammy might have gone.

"Well," said Sydney. "He did mention a few days ago that he wanted more adventure in his life."

This set Dumbo thinking. Where would a seal go if he wanted some adventure, he wondered. In a while it came to Dumbo — the sea, it was obvious!

"Come on, Timothy, climb aboard. We're off to the seaside!" said Dumbo.

"Good luck!" shouted Sydney, as Dumbo flew off as fast as he could. "Try to make it back for the evening show!" he added.

It was cold and dark when Dumbo and Timothy arrived over the sea. At first they couldn't see anything at all, then in the distance they saw a small figure on a rock, glistening in the moonlight.

"What's that over there?" said Timothy, pointing to the rock.

"Let's take a look!" said Dumbo as he swooped down over the sea. When they got closer, they heard a barking noise that sounded like a cry for help. Sure enough, it was Sammy, looking very cold and bedraggled.

"I'm so glad you found me!" he said. "I thought I wanted some adventure, but now all I want is to go back to my friends."

"No problem at all. Just hop on and we'll have you back in no time," replied Dumbo.

So the flying elephant gave Sammy a lift to the circus and they still managed to get back in time for the evening show. Everyone was very pleased to see Sammy back again. The circus manager even promised to take him and the other seals on an adventure holiday to the seaside every year. Dumbo was the hero of the day!

GOOFY
STACKS OF CANS

THUMPER'S LESSON

Bambi and his friend, Thumper, were walking through the forest. It was a cold, clear day, but as usual, Thumper was very bright and breezy. He couldn't stop talking as he bounced along. "What a lovely winter's day it is," he said to Bambi, "I feel so full of energy I could jump to the moon."

"Steady on," said Bambi, trying to calm his friend down. "You can't jump that far."

"Maybe not," said Thumper, "but I'm sure I could jump half way." Bambi didn't say anything, but thought to himself that Thumper, as usual, was getting carried away.

They walked on a little further and came to a ditch. Thumper started to get very excited, his little feet thumping the ground. "Look, look," he shouted. "I bet I could jump over that." Before

Bambi could stop him, the little rabbit ran up and bounced over the ditch.

"Hey, look at me!" he shouted as he flew across.

"Very good!" said Bambi. "Now how are you going to get back to this side?"

"Simple!" replied Thumper. "I'll just jump back over again." And that's exactly what he did, except this time he only just made it to the other side.

"I wish he'd stop showing off," thought Bambi. But Thumper didn't stop. In a while they came to a stream.

"It'll be easy to jump over this!" said Thumper. Bambi tried to stop the little rabbit.

"Don't be silly, you'll never make it across there!" he said. Thumper did not listen. He took a running jump and just managed to land on the other side.

"Look at me!" boasted Thumper. "I did it again." His little feet thumped up and down. Bambi frowned and walked away.

"If you think you're so clever," he said, "I'm going back home!"

"Hey, wait for me!" shouted Thumper. But at that moment, a log moved further upstream and the current started to go faster and faster. Thumper began to get frightened. He did not think he could jump across again.

"Bambi, help! I don't think I can make it!" he cried. Bambi turned around and saw that his little friend needed help. Without wasting any time, Bambi found a large fallen branch. He picked it up in his mouth and using all his strength, dragged it over to the stream. Then with one of his bird friends helping him, Bambi pushed the branch up against a tree and toppled it over, so that it made a bridge across the stream.

"Come on, Thumper, run across quickly," cried Bambi. Thumper plucked up all his courage and scampered across. When he got to the other side the little rabbit thanked Bambi.

"That's a lesson for you, Thumper: you should never show off, especially near water," said Bambi.

"You're right," agreed Thumper. "I won't do that again!"

Walt Disney's

SCAMP

CLEVER
CHATTY

THE END